Editorial and project management by
Shaila Shah, BAAF
Designed by Andrew Haig & Associates
Illustrations by Sarah Rawlings
Printed by The Lavenham Press, Suffolk

GW00866135

Nathan's
STORY

Children and families come in all shapes and sizes! Let's hear about some of
them. When you read Nathan's story, can you see if you can find Nathan in the
playground?

Introduction

When children are separated from their family of origin part of their very self is in jeopardy. No matter what their age or circumstances, that interruption of familiar and uniquely personal kinship ties can lead to potentially lifelong wounds. Adoption and fostering is not only about joining and welcoming, but also about grieving and losing as well as struggling and working together. Family life is never easy and new or reconstituted families have additional pressures and demands.

One of these is to help children to make sense of their often fragmented and confused experience. Their past is a crucial part of who they are and one of the key tasks for carers is to help children to integrate their past and their present. They are then able to move towards a future that builds on reality including the joys and sorrows which characterise all our stories. This task is not easy. So often the implicit message to permanent carers is to treat the child as if he or she were their own – and indeed that is necessary in order to build the quality of relationships that all parents hope for. Yet they are also asked never to forget that children are not their own – that they come from a different family with a different history.

Why this workbook?

The importance of helping children to make sense of their story is widely accepted. Each of us has a basic right to know who we are and where we come from. Children who cannot understand why they are separated will almost always take on the guilt and responsibility themselves. It is therefore vital that they are helped to make sense of their individual history. Life story books are valuable tools in this respect, but care needs to be taken that they are not reduced to little more than photograph albums. Children want to know not only what, but why, and information needs to be accurate, truthful, respectful and age/development appropriate.

This workbook is one amongst a collection relating to a number of children who are not living with their birth families. The stories each have a different scenario and it is hoped that they may act as useful triggers in a variety of settings. Experience shows that the reality of getting down to discussing and explaining is far from easy. Birth families, foster carers, adopters and social workers all struggle with the language and feelings involved. For birth families the pain and loss that is inherent in relinquishment can be overwhelming. Permanent carers can be fearful and avoidant of genuinely confronting a history which is not part of their shared experience. Social workers may be over-protective regarding difficult information and often feel lacking in communication skills. Therefore it is imperative that in order to use this workbook most effectively the reader is adequately prepared for the task.

Preparation

It is important to recognise that exploring painful and traumatic events with children evokes for each of us our own experience of loss or suffering. Learning to live with these events may be a lifelong task but we need at least to be on the journey before we can help a child to risk setting out. If there are areas of our life that remain too difficult to face we may need more time before embarking on working with children. Our fear, hesitancy or reluctance to face pain may well communicate itself to the child who will sense that difficult issues are best left unspoken and kept inside.

Some children may be overwhelmed by their experience, struggling with guilt, anger, sadness, responsibility, divided loyalties, and unsure of their capacity to survive emotionally. A sensitive, caring adult can acknowledge these feelings with the child, accepting but not minimising their confusion and hurt. Demonstrating a strength and resilience in the face of pain allows the child slowly to develop a sense of hope and conviction that all will be well. The stories in this series are about facts, but also about feelings, for the two cannot be separated. Adults need to be honest about their own emotions before they are able to help children with theirs.

In order to share a child's history it is essential to have as much accurate information as possible about their circumstances. Different tools may help to identify gaps in knowledge that ideally need to filled before embarking on life history work. For a fuller and more detailed account see BAAF's book, *Life Story Work*.

A *word of caution*

Some children with particularly difficult and traumatic histories may be unable for a variety of reasons to confront their past. Care should be exercised when children appear to be well defended and highly resistant to sharing previous experience. Sometimes such children may be receiving therapeutic help to explore painful issues and this may be a long-term process. Children – and adults – maintain their defences for a purpose and they deserve a healthy respect. These stories are potential channels whereby connections may be made, feelings shared, hopes and fears discussed and attachment encouraged. They should never be used in an intrusive way that fails to respect the child's wishes and anxieties. All adults can do is to open doors; it is the child who decides whether or not to pass through.

Using the workbook

The workbooks in this series are specific and are therefore inevitably limited in their direct application. Every story line is unique and there can be few common denominators. However, the range extends across a variety of familiar scenarios and backgrounds, and while they may require adjustment given individual circumstances, it is hoped that they may also be helpful triggers. In some cases carers or professionals may be able to use them as they stand; alternatively they may prove helpful in enabling adults to rehearse a specific storyline that relates to a particular child, or children can be encouraged to note the differences/similarities between their own stories and those of the children featured.

Various tools have been incorporated into the story and the work sheets at the end are further aids to helping children explore issues and feelings. Both the work sheets and story can be used flexibly and can therefore be moved around in different combinations. It will be important for adults to consider the individual needs of each child. The workbook reflects a multicultural population and many children will require additional information concerning, for example, their racial, cultural and religious heritage; preverbal children will be more able to identify with play techniques and very simple story lines; learning disabled children may make greater use of visual content than the written word. Each child will have his or her own needs and story and the workbook is meant to be used creatively and flexibly in conjunction with the many other useful tools already available.

Birth parents, carers and social workers may find the story lines helpful to use with children as part of preparation work, within family placements, or at key times such as adoption hearings or disruption. Specific (future) stories may be helpful to families preparing their own children for adoption or fostering, stepfamilies who are adopting and those who may be helping their children to understand relinquishment of a sibling. Guardians, residential workers, family centres and day nurseries may find relevant scenarios that could be useful in their work with children and young people and there is an educational value in raising community awareness of children's needs and the range of situations represented within adoption and fostering.

Explaining and exploring

Life is a continual story and the task of story telling is never complete. As the child grows and develops so too will his or her understanding of their situation. Histories will need to be repeated, reworked and more carefully explained as comprehension becomes more sophisticated. It is important to use developmentally appropriate language and concepts and be aware of the need to refine and adapt material according to each child's needs and abilities. It is important to listen to children – to hear what it is they want to know and to avoid the temptation to convey too much too quickly. Stories evolve, often from short conversations about people, places, times, events. Children will often not need the elaborate explanations that adults prepare. Equally, it is dangerous to wait until children ask questions before imparting information; some never will and need permission to broach such personal issues. Such permission is not only verbal, but manifests itself in so many of our unspoken attitudes and responses to the child's history.

Visual aids such as this workbook are only one small contribution to the child's ongoing task of making sense of who they are. Direct and indirect contact with the child's family members can be a major source of information and encourage a realistic and developing understanding of what has happened and why. For permanently placed children the biggest factor will be their carer's ability to embrace both them and their history, knowing that they are one and the same. Our background may be complex and painful but sharing that experience over time within an environment of safety, acceptance and affirmation is the way to healing and emotional growth.

Nathan's STORY

Nathan is four and has just started at Greenfield School. He likes his teacher, Mr Bannister, and hopes that he can stay at Greenfield for a long time. He doesn't want to move any more.

This is Nathan's story.

The first person that Nathan lived with was Rose. Nathan grew in Rose's tummy, so she was his **birth mummy**. After he was born Rose took him home from hospital. He was a beautiful baby. But Rose found it very hard to be a mummy. Nathan's daddy, Marcus, came from a Jamaican family like Rose. Marcus wasn't ready to be a daddy. He didn't come and see them and Rose was very lonely.

Looking after babies is hard work. They need lots of cuddles, talking and playing. They also need to be fed, changed and kept safe. It is very important to look after babies so they can grow up to be strong.

Rose tried very hard. The **social worker** gave her lots of help. Social workers are people who try to help grown ups and children when they are unhappy. Nathan was very thin and he looked sad. He was spending lots of time on his own and he cried a lot. Rose was unhappy too. She told the social worker that she loved Nathan. She wanted to look after him but didn't think she could be a good mummy.

The social worker helped Nathan to understand what this felt like for his mum. Many grown ups and children have some things they can't do, even though they want to…. Nathan wants to ride a bike, but he keeps falling off! He wants to play with his friend's computer games, but he knows that he must wait until he is older. And he wants to be a great footballer like Ian Wright, but he doesn't know if he will ever be that good!

Rose talked to the social worker for a long time about Nathan. She was very sad because she knew she could not give him all the loving and caring he needed. Rose asked the social worker if she could find someone to look after Nathan while she decided what to do.

So Nathan went to live with Tom and Delores, who are foster carers, and their two children. Foster carers look after children until they can go home or move on to a new family.

Tom, Delores and their family loved Nathan. They gave him many cuddles and had lots of time to play with him.

Nathan started to grow bigger and looked much happier. Rose
came to visit him sometimes. He looked forward to seeing
her and she was really pleased with
how well he looked.

Rose wanted Nathan to be happy always. She had tried to be a mummy but it
had been very hard. So she asked the social worker to find a new family for
him where he could grow up and belong.

Rose thought that Nathan's new family should be black, like Nathan, and be a happy family with lots of love to share. Rose met Marlene and her family and she thought they were just right. They talked about Nathan and how much Rose wanted him to be part of a family.

Nathan met Marlene and her daughter, Sophie, when he was two and a half. They came to visit him at his foster home. Nathan liked living with Tom and Delores and it took a while to get to know his new family. But Marlene was very nice and Nathan liked playing "catch the ball" with Sophie.

Nathan visited the house where Marlene and Sophie lived. He met Grannie and Aunty Bea who also live there. Nathan loved listening to their stories about growing up.

Nathan liked staying with Marlene and started to leave some of his toys there. Marlene asked Nathan if he would like to live with her all the time and he said "yes!" Nathan was sad to say goodbye to Tom and Delores but they said they would come and visit him.

Before Nathan moved, Rose came to say goodbye. Although she was sad, she was also pleased to see him so happy about living with his new family.

Nathan moved to Marlene's house and it soon felt like home.

He loved the tasty patties that Marlene made and Sophie showed him pictures of Jamaica, where Rose comes from. And Grannie and Aunty Bea told him stories at bedtime.

After a while, Marlene talked to Nathan about **adoption**. It was a hard word to understand but Nathan knew it meant that he would always be part of this family. Marlene helped Nathan draw pictures of Rose and then his new family.

When Nathan was four he went to see the **judge** with Marlene and Sophie. They asked the judge if Nathan could be adopted into their family.

Judges are wise people who have to decide about very important things like adoption. The judge said that she was pleased Nathan was happy with Marlene and Sophie and yes, he could be adopted.

Everyone was very happy. When they got home they had a big party to celebrate.

Nathan still sees Tom and Delores and their children. Marlene helps him write letters to Rose and they send her pictures. She knows Nathan is doing well and loves the photo of him in his Arsenal shirt.

Nathan knows that being adopted means he belongs to a new family and that they will look after him while he grows up. But he knows that his birth family, especially Rose, will always be special.

something to remember…

Adoption means belonging to a new family but it doesn't mean forgetting people you know and love.

special words

Birth mummy and birth daddy are the mummy and daddy who make the child that grows in mummy's tummy.

A **social worker** is someone who tries to help children and their families when they are unhappy; they also try to find new parents for children who need them.

A **foster carer** usually looks after children for a while until they can go home or move on to a new family.

Adoption means belonging to and growing up with a new family when children cannot live with their birth family.

A **judge** is a wise person who makes important decisions about where children live and whom they should live with if grown ups cannot agree.

Worksheet

1 The first person that Nathan lived with was his birth mummy, Rose. Who are your birth mummy and birth daddy? Do you remember them? Can you draw something about them?

_____

_____

_____

_____

2 This is Nathan's new family – Marlene, Sophie, Grannie and Aunty Bea. Can you draw your new family?

3 Nathan understands that there are some things you can't do, even though you want to. Is there anything that you can't do but would like to?

_____

_____

_____

_____

_____

4 Nathan found it hard to leave Tom and Delores to live with Marlene. Have you ever had to leave someone you cared about? How did it make you feel? Who did you talk to?

_____

_____

_____

_____

_____

5 Marlene helps Nathan to write to Rose and talk about her. Do you write to anyone? Is there someone you think of a lot and remember?

_____

_____

_____

_____

_____

_____

6 When Nathan was adopted, the family had a big party to celebrate. When did you last have a party? What were you celebrating? Who was invited to the party? What did you like best about it?

_____

_____

_____

_____

_____

_____

_____